BIBLE TIMES
in Riddles & Rhymes

· · · · · · · · · · · ·

A Fun Way to
Share and Remember
Well-Known
Bible Stories

SYLVIA TAYLOR-STEIN

ILLUSTRATED BY WILSON GANDOLPHO

Bible Times in Riddles & Rhymes
ISBN 978-0-9994061-0-6

Printed in the United States of America.

Produced by The Denzel Agency (www.denzel.org)
Cover and Interior Design: Rob Williams

Bible Times Publishing
sylvia@bibletimespublishing.com
www.bibletimespublishing.com

CONTENTS

DEDICATION

To my Grandma Lottie, who was the greatest storyteller ever. She instilled in me a love for Bible heroes and heroines through her wonderful gift of storytelling.

To Marc, my wonderful husband, who has never stopped encouraging me in writing this book, and who inspires me every day.

To Jackson, whose love for riddles ignited my desire to create a fun way and a game for him to learn some of the most significant stories in the Bible.

To my wonderful children and grandchildren, Troy, Beth, Trevor, Alyssa, Ethan, and Jackson. You are such a blessing.

To my Lord and Savior, Jesus Christ, for saving me; to God, my Father, for giving me life; and to the Holy Spirit, for giving me words when I could not find them.

PREFACE

This book is made up of riddles and rhymes that will help grandparents, parents, children and grandchildren connect, spend time studying God's Word, and remember the stories of Scripture. Here's the story behind *Bible Times in Riddles & Rhymes*.

This book happened after a very busy and fun-filled weekend with our grandson with a lot of time spent solving riddles. He got on the iPhone and kept belting us with riddles. It turned out to be a really fun and stimulating way to spend some time in the car and tax our brains trying to solve some of the ones that he loved to throw at us. We took him home, and the next morning while praying, and reflecting on the blessed weekend, and what a gift it was to have such quality time with him, the thought came to me, *Why not use this fun mode to teach him about the Bible and God?* I recalled sitting in my grandma's kitchen as a little girl, enjoying her wonderful storytelling of Bible stories. She had such a gift for telling stories and making them come alive. She was my first real introduction to the Bible, and it occurred to me that with my grandson's love for riddles, why not put some of these well-known Bible stories in riddle and rhyme form and use these as a game with him. We gave him a little incentive to get 100 points: he receives 2 points for each riddle and is rewarded with a prize at the end. As I write this he has accumulated 40 points and is on his way to 100.

From that weekend, this book came into being. I never forgot the Bible stories my grandmother taught me, and my hope is that these riddles will help many children, parents and grandparents connect and spend time studying God's Word in riddle and rhyme form.

These riddles and rhymes follow a rather chronologically loose order from Genesis through the Gospels. I just wrote them as they came to me and I know there are many more stories that could be shared, and I hope to do so in the future. I pray this book of riddles and rhymes will be an inspiration to you and your family.

~ 1 ~

THE COUPLE

They were a beautiful couple, perfectly created
And in a lovely garden, they were blissfully situated

They lived among the animals of every sort and breed
Where they could play, enjoy, care, and feed

A special bond they had with their Creator too
He walked with them in the evening and taught them what to do

He said, "I've given you the run of this beautiful garden zoo
But one thing I command, that you must never do

There's a tree in this garden, don't touch it, or eat its fruit
For in the day you do, I will have to give you the boot."

Now the serpent was very slick and caught the woman unaware
She ate, and then her mate, both fell into his lair

Their eyes were suddenly opened; they hid from God in shame
He made them clothes of hides and sent them far away

. . . .

Who is this couple?

What did the serpent tell the woman would happen if she ate from the tree?

Why did God tell them not to eat of this tree?

Why did they disobey God and eat from it?

What was the name of the tree?

. . . .

GENESIS 2:15-17; 3:6-9

2

TWO BROTHERS

They were the first two babies born to their dad and mother
Firstborn son was Cain, then Abel, his younger brother

The brothers prepared a sacrifice that was sure to please their God
Abel, a firstborn lamb; Cain, fruit from tilling the sod

God accepted Abel's gift, but Cain's He did decline
That sent Cain into a tiff, and he began to whine

The more he whined, the madder he got; his plan began to brew:
I'll meet my brother in the field, and him I will undo

The firstborn son did his deed and brought grief to his dad and mother
By this act he sealed his fate, when he _____ his younger_____.

. . . .

What did Cain do?

What wrong emotion caused Cain to do this?

How can we guard against this emotion in our lives?

What should we do when others do well?

. . . .

Genesis 4:1-8

(Answers: murdered, brother)

～ 3 ～

A BIG BOAT

Living in a land of sin that grieved him every day
This righteous man was living right, and trying to obey

One day God said to him, "I'm destroying this wicked place.
A flood will cover every inch, only you and your family I'll save."

God told him how to build a boat, such as there had never been
At this time, rain did not fall, so people scoffed and ridiculed him

He built the boat, the animals came, entering two by two
God closed the window and the door, and the storm began to brew

Water covered the entire earth; only those in the boat remained
When the land was dry, they came out, to repopulate the earth again

God said that never again would He destroy the earth with a flood
He put a sign in the sky; it reminds us His promise is good

· ·

Who was the man who built the boat?

Why did God send the flood?

What did God put in the sky?

What was His promise?

· ·

GENESIS 6, 7, 8

~ 4 ~

THE SACRIFICE

He had waited so long for God to send the promised one
His love for him knew no bounds, for this long-awaited son

One day God instructed him, take this son you love so much
Up to that far mountain, and there sacrifice him as such

He trusted God with all his heart, knowing His promises would stand
That even if he should slay his son, God could raise him up again

But before he accomplished the deed that he knew he had to do
An angel stayed his hand and said, "God sees your love is true

That you would give your only son, proves your total love for Me
In you all nations will be blessed, and your offspring more than the sands of the sea."

. . . .

Who is the father?

Who is the son?

What does "in your offspring, all nations will be blessed" mean?

. . . .

GENESIS 22:1-18

5

SLAVE TO A KING

He was the favorite son of his father and mother
But he was despised and hated by his many brothers
So they devised a plan to get rid of him for good
Sold him to some traders passing through the neighborhood

They lied to their poor father, said he was killed by some wild thing
His father wept and mourned him, but they would not come clean
He ended up in jail for something he did not do
Thirteen years imprisoned, but his heart to God stayed true

Fast forward many years, and he is renowned throughout the land
He's second to the king, and all must do as he commands
A great famine is coming, of which God through him foretold
And he's prepared for the shortage, abundant grain will be sold

His father sends the brothers to buy, so that they may eat
They did not know that the brother they sold, they would get to meet
He invites them to a banquet, where they are served the finest fare
At the highest table he listens from his royal chair

He learns he has a younger brother whom he does not know
And his father is doing well but still misses him so
When he can no longer stand it, he goes alone to cry
Lost years and lost memories, but he knows the reason why

God used for great good, all the evil they intended
His broken, betrayed heart, being divinely mended
For God had sent him on ahead so that his family may be saved
By the one, God made a king, who once was a slave

. . . .

Who is this?

Why did the brothers hate him?

How did the brothers respond when they realized the king was their brother?

. . . .

GENESIS 37–45

~ 6 ~

THE BABY BOY

He was a beautiful baby whom his parents tried to hide
Because the wicked king sent an order, baby boys he would not abide

But his parents believed in God and did not fear the king's command
They hid him for three months until they made their plan

They placed him in a basket, on the river's side
A daughter had pity upon him when she heard his cries

His mother's faith was rewarded, as she got to raise her son
Then he moved into the palace as the daughter's adopted one

He grew up to be Prince of Egypt, but his people, Israel, he did love
Saved them from this wicked king; God spoke to him from heaven above

. . . .

Who is this baby boy?

Who is the daughter?

Who is the king?

. . . .

EXODUS 2:1-10

7

FREEDOM

He was getting on in years when God gave him the call:
"Go to Egypt. Set My people free. I'll be with you through it all."

The people were sorely treated, in bondage 400 years
The land drenched in their sweat, suffering bathed in tears

"God says to let His people go," he told the pagan ruler
The ruler retorted in contempt, "I'll make their bondage crueler."

God sent plagues upon the land, horrible and painful for sure
But the king was very stubborn, and dug in his heels even more

It took the last dreadful plague before the evil ruler caved
The people left Egypt with much joy, to no longer be enslaved

. . . .

Who was the man?

Who were the people?

Why did the king refuse to let the people go after each plague?

Why did the king finally give in?

. . . .

EXODUS 3:10-12; 4:1-17; 7:14–12:32

8

THE MIRACLE

They had no place to run, pushed up against the sea
Pharaoh's army driving hard, they cried out desperately

God instructed Moses, "Hold up the staff that's in your hand."
The sea parted before their eyes; Israel crossed on dry land

But not so for Pharaoh's army, who hoped Israel to enslave again
The staff was lowered, and his great army was covered in water and sand

For the sea came crashing down on them, God in His power had spoken
The children of Israel were saved that day, and slavery's yoke was broken

. . . .

Why did Pharaoh chase the children of Israel?

What was God trying to teach His people in this miracle?

. . . .

EXODUS 14:1-29

PSALM 106:9-11

9

RIGHTEOUS ANGER

Moses went up the mountain, as God did command
To get two stone tablets, words inscribed by God's own hand

He delayed his return; the people began to murmur and hiss,
"We want a god we can worship, for we don't know where Moses is."

They were so determined, Moses' brother finally gave in
He melted all their gold, and fashioned it into an idol of sin

Moses came off the mountain, carrying the tablets with God's commands
The people were worshiping a golden calf and committing wholesale sin

Moses' rage was inflamed, his fury knew no bounds
He lost it with the people, smashed the tablets on the ground

The people were disciplined and they repented, the commands written again
As a covenant between God and His people, to forever stand

. . . .

Why did Moses delay coming off the mountain?

Why did the people resort to idol worship?

How did God discipline them?

. . . .

EXODUS 24:18; 31:18; 32:1-19,30-35

⤳ 10 ⤲

THE SPIES

Twelve were sent to search the land that God had promised to give them
The land was rich and fertile, but inhabited by great big men

Back at camp, ten spies said, "Yes, the land is lush and filled with plenty.
But huge people live there; we can't defeat them, there are too many."

But two spies opposed what the others said. "We can take it," they began their plea,
"for God is with us; He will provide." But the people would not agree

Instead they listened to the other spies, who were full of dread and fear
They threatened to stone the two faithful spies, but then the glory of the Lord appeared

He said, "Because you have not trusted in Me, nor believed My faithful spies,
In the wilderness you'll wander 40 more years until all of you have died."

. . . .

Who were the two faithful spies who said God would provide?

What caused the ten spies to tell the people not to try to take the land?

What can we learn from their story?

. . . .

NUMBERS 13:1-3,25-33; 14:6-10,34

❧ 11 ❧

THE DONKEY

He was sent to curse God's people, and started down the hill
He was well into his mission when his donkey stopped dead still

He whipped his donkey three times, but she would not start
And when the donkey began to talk, it almost stopped his heart

The donkey said, "Why do you beat me, when I have served you from a foal.
Have I ever abused you in any way, or not done what I was told?"

Then the man's eyes were opened, and he saw what had stood in his way
He fell face down on the ground and repented that very day

. . . .

Who was the man who was sent to curse God's people?

Why did the donkey stop?

What was in the road and what did it say?

What did the man do?

. . . .

NUMBERS 22:7,12,21-31

~ 12 ~

THE STRONG MAN

He was young and strong; God gave him special strength
Found in his massive hair, that was very long in length

The secret of his strength was in his manly tresses
As long as he never cut it, God told him He would bless it

But he had a great weakness, bad women he did crave
One in particular would surely make him a slave

She said, "Tell me the secret of your strength," but he would not reveal
She whimpered and she whined, but he was resolute still

But her endless nagging wore him down; he finally told her about his hair
While asleep she cut it, and his strength vanished in thin air

His enemies put him in a temple, and blinded him forever
His hair grew back, so did his strength
And their demise exemplifies: they were not so clever

. . . .

Who is this man?

Who is the woman?

Who are his enemies?

Why did he tell the woman the secret of his strength?

What happened after his hair grew back?

What did he do?

. . . .

JUDGES 16:4-30

13

THE GLEANER

They set out for Israel, two weary widows from a foreign land
The mother-in-law going home, the younger clinging to her hand

They had come home empty and hungry; everything was gone
The younger said, "I will glean in the fields; we will get along."

She worked all day in the fields; the owner, a kind man, let her stay
He said, "Leave her a little extra, and do not send her away."

She lived with Naomi, her mother-in-law by name
She fell in love with this kind man, and one they soon became

She is the great-grandmother of another courageous man of fame
God called him a man after His own heart: _____ is his name

. . . .

What is her name?

Who did she marry?

Who is her great-grandson? (Fill in the blank.)

Who is her greatest offspring?

. . . .

RUTH 1:6–4:22

MATTHEW 1:5-6

(Answer: David)

～ 14 ～

A BOY IS CALLED

He was only a little boy, serving an old prophet of the Lord
He worked in the Lord's house every day, but had not yet received the word

One night as he was sleeping, he heard someone call his name
He ran to the bedside of the prophet, and said, "You called; I came."

The third time this happened, the prophet said, "This is of the Lord.
Tell Him to speak and you will listen." The boy did and received the word

The word was not good for the old prophet; his sins God could no longer stand
But the boy was blessed by God and, in time, became the greatest prophet in the land

· · · · · · · · · · · · · · · · · · · ·

Who is the boy?

Who is the old prophet?

What was the old prophet's sin?

Why was he held responsible for what his sons did?

· · · · · · · · · · · · · · · · · · · ·

1 SAMUEL 3:1-21

15

THE CHOSEN ONE

God told the prophet Samuel, "To Bethlehem you must go.
I have chosen a son of Jesse, when you see him you will know."

When Samuel got to Bethlehem, he invited Jesse and his sons
To join him in a sacrifice, where he would anoint the chosen one

All seven sons before Samuel passed, but God said, "These aren't the one."
"Are there any others?" Samuel asked. "Just the shepherd, my youngest son."

"Send for him," Samuel said. "We'll not sit down until he comes."
When he entered the room, God told Samuel, "This is the chosen one."

Samuel poured the oil upon his head, his Dad and brothers stood apart
He was anointed the king of Israel and he was a man after God's own heart

. . . .

Who was the boy?

Why did Jesse not bring him in with the other sons at the beginning?

What can we learn from this?

. . . .

1 SAMUEL 16:1-13

~ 16 ~

THE GIANT SLAYER

Take these supplies to your brothers; find out how the war is going
Come back with a report; I need to know how they are doing

The boy came upon Israel's army, entrenched upon a rise
A giant shouting from the valley, "Hey, cowards, send me someone to fight!

And I will give him to the buzzards, after I tear him limb from limb!"
Terrified of the giant, no man would dare go up against him

The boy came upon the scene, and he was filled with fury
How dare this pig challenge the living God: "I will take him down in a hurry!"

He met the giant, boldly saying, "I come in the name of my God and Lord."
He placed a rock in his sling and planted it squarely in the giant's forehead

Israel's army had a great victory; the blasphemous giant was dead
When the other army saw what happened, every one of them turned and fled

. . . .

Who is this boy?

What happened to him after that?

Why did the boy not fear the giant?

. . . .

1 SAMUEL 17:12-50

~ 17 ~

THE QUEEN

The word went out far and wide: find the most beautiful of girls
The king was looking for that special one, who would surely rock his world

He thought the decision was his alone, but God had a different plan
The queen would be God's choice, and fulfill His purpose in the land

God's choice became the queen; her beauty was renowned
Her faith in God was strong; on her head she wore the royal crown

But an evil man wanted to kill her kin: his sinister plot he laid
She got word of this from her uncle, and for three days fasted and prayed

Her courage brought truth to light; her people God did save
But the evil man got his just desserts, and went to an early grave

. . . .

Who is the queen?

Who are her people?

Who is the evil man?

Who told the queen about the evil man's plans?

How did God save her people?

What can we learn from her?

. . . .

ESTHER 2:2-4,16-17; 3:5-6; 4:15-16; 7:1-6,10

∽ 18 ∾

WORTH

Her price is far above rubies, is what the teacher said
Her husband safely trusts in her; her presence makes him glad

She's a smart, industrious woman, who works diligently and well
She wisely feeds and clothes her children; she knows how to buy and sell

Her husband's known, and well respected, by those in their town
He has a confidence that shows; she doesn't let him down

She speaks with love and kindness; her words do not destroy
Whoever seeks and finds her, will know real peace and joy

There are many who'll call her blessed, most especially those she's raised
Charm and beauty come to an end, but a godly woman will always be praised

. . . .

Why is a woman like this considered rare?

Does she sound like someone you know?

What traits does she have that we can emulate?

. . . .

PROVERBS 31:10-31

19

FAITH

Three Hebrew boys in a pagan land, to their God vowed to be true
Their trust was strong and resilient; they were faithful through and through

But evil men laid a sinister plot: to kill them was their objective
Appealing to the king's vanity would accomplish their wicked directive

Arrogant king made a decree: no god could be worshiped but him
The boys would not bow down; so a fiery furnace was prepared for them

Bound, they were thrown into the flames, but when the king looked he was stunned
Three were thrown in the fire, but now a fourth one walked among

He hastened to bring the three boys out; they were not burned or singed at all
The king knew then their God was God, and before him he did humbly fall

. . . .

What happened to the evil men?

Who was the fourth man in the fire?

What can we learn from the three boys?

. . . .

DANIEL 3:1-30

20

CAPTIVE

He was just a lad when he was taken from his home
But he became famous in a kingdom that was pagan to the bone

God gave him many gifts, great wisdom one bestowed
But jealous governors hated him, and said this guy must go!

So they set a nasty trap, appealed to the king's great vanity:
"Let no one pray but to you, oh king. Let that be your decree."

The captive prayed only to God, every day three times
Wicked men turned him in, demanding he pay for his praying crime

The king was very sad, for the captive he loved well
But a king's decree could not be changed; death by lions would prevail

The lions were very hungry, impatiently waiting for their meal
The captive said, "My God will save me, and I know I won't be killed.

He'll protect me from their fangs; on me they will not dine."
The captive was thrown into the den, and the lions behaved just fine

The lions became very calm, when before they were in a ravenous strut
But God performed a miracle when their _____ He did _____.

. . . .

Who is the captive?

Can you finish the rhyme? (The second blank rhymes with "strut.")

What can we learn from the captive's story?

. . . .

DANIEL 6:1-28

(Answers: mouths, shut)

21

THE RUNAWAY

God gave him an urgent message to take to the sinful hood
He did not want to go and said, "For me this can't be good."

He began to plan and scheme, decided to run away
Headed out to sea, on a boat set sail that day

A storm arose, the waves did pound, the sailors were a wreck
The runaway cried, "It's all my fault! Throw me off the deck!"

They did as he asked, the sea became calm, but something was amiss
As he plunged head first into the sea, he was swallowed by a fish

Three days later, he got belched up, and learned his lesson good
When God gives you a message, you better take it to the hood

. . . .

Who was the runaway?

What message did God have for this particular hood?

What does this story teach us about God?

. . . .

JONAH 1:1-17; 2:10; 3:1-10

22

THE VIRGIN

She was just a young girl, living in the hills of Galilee
But chosen for a special purpose, to fulfill the prophecy

She was especially selected, above all of womankind
God's Son she would bear, and this would be the special sign

The spirit of God would overshadow her, and she would conceive
Although a virgin, she trusted God, and this miracle she believed

It came to pass that she was with child, and God's only begotten Son
Would come into the world through her, this young virgin

She shared with her fiancé, a just and honorable man
But thinking he made a mistake, he decided not to take her hand

Then an angel told him in a dream, "Do not hesitate.
The child she carries is from God, and He will be very great."

He was born in a stable, no room for them in the inn
Into the world he came to deliver us from sin

His mission started in a stall among the sheep and dung
Through a chosen virgin, God's salvation work was begun

· · · · · · · · · · · · · · · ·

Who is the girl?

Why do you think God chose her?

Who is the baby?

Where was her baby born?

Why is this baby's birth so important?

· · · · · · · · · · · · · · · ·

LUKE 1:26-38; 2:6-20

⤎ 23 ⤏

FATHER'S BUSINESS

They had traveled for a day and missed Him in the crowd
They searched among their kinfolk and called His name out loud

They headed back to Jerusalem, and searched for Him three days
They were filled with fear, and so worried if He was safe

He was nowhere to be seen; all their steps they did retrace
Back from whence they'd come, they found Him in this place

He was sitting among the teachers, listening and asking questions
The teachers were amazed at His wisdom and deep perception

They were most astonished at this their 12-year-old son
And said, "How could you treat us like this? We are so undone."

He said, "Why have you been searching for Me? Don't you know what I must do?
I must be in My Father's house, and it's His business I must see to."

His mother treasured His words in her heart, although they didn't yet understand,
But He grew in wisdom and stature, and in favor with God and man

. . . .

Who were they looking for?

Where did they find Him?

What did He mean about doing His Father's business?

. . . .

LUKE 2:39-52

24

THE PROPHET

He didn't come from royalty
The wilderness was his home
Wore a coat of camel's hair
Ate honey in the comb

Some wondered if he was the Christ
His preaching fervent and vigorous
Some called him the wild prophet
Others thought him much too rigorous

He wasn't the Christ, but paved the way
As the prophets declared he would
He baptized the real Christ in the Jordan
As he was told he should

. . . .

Who is the prophet?

Who is the Christ?

Why was Christ baptized?

. . . .

LUKE 3:1-21

MATTHEW 3:1-17

❦ 25 ❦

TEMPTATION

Jesus had fasted 40 days, and He was very weak
Satan said, "Turn these stones to bread, and You'll have plenty to eat."

Jesus said, "Man does not live by bread alone, but by God's every word."
Satan, undaunted, devised another test that he was sure would work

He took Him to a pinnacle and said, "Jump off here.
We know His angels will bear You up. You have nothing to fear."

But Jesus, knowing his cunning ways, and the evil he did suggest
Declared, "I will not tempt the Lord, My God, and put Him to the test!"

But Satan was not done with Jesus, and hit Him with his best shot
He said, "All the world's kingdoms I'll give You, if You'll worship me on the spot."

Jesus said, "Away with you, Satan; don't you know what the Scriptures say?
Worship the Lord God, and Him alone, and serve Him every day."

. . . .

Why did Satan tempt Jesus?

Why did God allow him to?

In what three ways did Satan tempt Jesus?

What can we learn from Jesus to help us when we are tempted?

. . . .

MATTHEW 4:1-11

26

WATER TO WINE

It was His first miracle at a wedding, where He was a guest
The wine was almost gone, a real downer for a love fest

His mother said, "Please help us, the party needs more wine."
Jesus said, "Don't you know that it isn't yet My time?"

He said, "Bring Me those jars, and with water, fill them to the rim."
Where water had gone in, red wine now flowed in abundance out from them

The banquet master was most impressed, he told the bridegroom with a grin,
"The best wine is served at the start of the feast, but you have saved the best till the end."

This was Jesus' first miracle that would reveal His power
His disciples saw and they believed, from that very hour

. . . .

Why did Jesus' mother ask Him for wine?

Why did Jesus say it wasn't His time?

Why did He go ahead and perform the miracle?

. . . .

JOHN 2:1-11

~ 27 ~

THANKFULNESS

Jesus was heading to Jerusalem when He came upon a sight
Ten lepers cried out, "Master, please heal us from our plight!"

When Jesus saw them, He had mercy: "Go show the priests in town."
As they hurried off, they became clean, but only one, a Samaritan, turned around

Praising God, he rushed back to Jesus; worshiping, he fell face down on the sod
Jesus said, "Where are the other nine that were healed?
Only this foreigner returns to thank God?"

. . . .

What excuses might the others have had for not returning and thanking Jesus?

What is Jesus trying to teach us in this miracle?

In what ways do we show our thankfulness to God?

. . . .

LUKE 17:11-19

-∾ 28 ∿-

BELIEF

The sea was crashing; the boat was tossed; the disciples cried out with fright
They tried to keep the boat afloat, but dismal seemed their plight

Jesus came to them, walking on waves. "It's a ghost!" some said on board
But as He came closer, they could clearly see that it was the Lord

Peter said, "Let me come to You." And by faith he walked on water
But then he started thinking, and that's when Peter began sinking

Jesus said, "Peter, you need to have faith," as He pulled him from the sea.
"You can do this, and so much more, if you only will believe!"

. . . .

Why did Peter start to sink?

What was Jesus trying to teach him?

What can we learn from Peter when we are in situations that require us to have faith?

. . . .

MATTHEW 14:22-33

29

WHAT YOU LOVE

Jesus said, "If you live for this, it will end up taking you out.
You can't serve it and serve God too, of that there is no doubt.

Once you fall into its trap, it becomes a powerful master;
And when it takes control, you are headed for disaster!"

Jesus warned us so that we would heed and remember and be strong
Serving this takes us away from God, and loving this is the root of all wrong

. . . .

What is Jesus warning us about?

Why is loving this the root of all evil?

. . . .

MATTHEW 6:24

~ 30 ~

BEAUTIFUL CLOTHES

The disciples worried about many things: what to eat and what to wear,
Where to lodge for the night, and how they would fare

Jesus said, "Don't worry about such things. That's what the world cares for.
Our Father will take care of all those things, on that you can be sure."

Jesus told them to consider the lily; it does not spin or sow
Yet it is more beautifully dressed than a king's fine clothes, you know

It doesn't worry about what to wear, because it's God, you see,
Who nurtures it and cares for it, and dresses it perfectly

. . . .

Why did Jesus use the example of the lily to explain worry?

What is Jesus telling us not to do in this passage?

. . . .

LUKE 12:22-28

❧ 31 ❧

TWO PATHS

There are two paths that we can walk as we make it through our life
One is wide and filled with pleasure and ease,
the other, bounded on every side

If we want to live with Jesus, stay away from the path that's wide
The bounded path leads to eternal life, and He will walk it by our side

. . . .

What is the bounded path?

Why does Jesus tell us to take this path?

. . . .

MATTHEW 7:13-14

32

TWO HOUSES

When storms and gales do roar, there will be no ill
Because this house is standing tough, ever strong and still

But down the road's another house, on a foundation, not so cool
It's slipping and shaking in the storm and looking like a tool

Two houses standing in a storm, one will fall with a crashing shock
The other one will not budge at all because it's built on solid_____

. . . .

What was the strong house built on?

Can you fill in the blank? (It rhymes with "shock.")

What foundation are we building our life on?

. . . .

MATTHEW 7:24-27

LUKE 6:46-49

(Answer: rock)

33

THE SON

He came to his dad, and there he demanded.
"Give me what's mine!" he loudly commanded

His dad did as he wished, and he went on his way
To a distant village, where he gambled and played

Later, when all his money was flushed down the drain
He found that loser friends leave when there's nothing to gain

Starving and broke, his life now a big mess
He said, "I will go to my dad and confess."

His dad saw him far off, gave him a greeting so hearty
He said, "My lost son is found. Let's have a big party!"

But the older brother wasn't happy, because he'd never had a fest
And now his brat brother was being treated like a royal guest

His father said to his oldest son, "Don't be angry and mad
All I have is yours too, and I am to both of you 'Dad.'

Let's celebrate together, from sin your brother is set free
He has repented and come home, to live with you and me."

· · · · · · · · · · · · · · · · · · ·

Who is the son?

What did his dad do when he came home?

Why was the good son angry?

What emotion did he exhibit?

How is the dad like our heavenly Dad?

· · · · · · · · · · · · · · · · · · ·

LUKE 15:11-32

34

THE WELL

They were heading to the village, when He sat down at a well
He told the others to go on ahead, as He watched a woman with a pail

It was noon, and she was alone; she had come to fetch some water
To Jacob's well she came, a lonely Samaritan daughter

Jesus asked her for a drink; she said, "But how can You?
Jews don't talk to Samaritans, this much I know is true."

Jesus said, "If you knew who speaks to you, you would know I have better water.
Anyone who drinks from your well will thirst again, my daughter."

He then began to tell her all about the life she'd led
She was very much astonished at everything He said

She ran back to the village, and cried, "You all must come!
I met a man. He's a prophet, and He told me everything I've done."

Jesus stayed there many days, preaching the good news for all to hear
Many believed on Him, and His words fell on welcoming ears

. . . .

Who was the woman?

What kind of water was Jesus talking about?

Why did He say that if you drink this different water you will never thirst again?

The Samaritans were enemies of the Jews,
so why did Jesus reach out to them with the salvation message?

. . . .

JOHN 4:4-15,28-30

35

THE POOR WIDOW

She came into the temple and had only a couple of pennies
For her offering to God; she was poor and didn't have plenty

To the offering box, the wealthy came, giving just what they thought they should
She walked up slowly to the box, and dropped in all her livelihood

Jesus, watching from nearby, said her offering was truly the best
She put in all she had; they put in a little and kept for themselves the rest

· · · · · · · · · · · · · · · · · ·

What did the poor widow put into the treasury?

Why did Jesus say her offering was greater than those
who put in much more than she?

· · · · · · · · · · · · · · · · · ·

MARK 12:41-44 44

36

HAVING
TOO MUCH

His crop came in and it was a whopper
His barn couldn't begin to store
All the harvest of such abundance
With so much he wanted more

So bigger barns he would build
And store it all for himself
"I can enjoy my surplus, with nothing to fear.
There'll be no bareness on my shelf."

Christ said, "You are a foolish man!
Death is standing outside your door.
You only thought of yourself
When you could have shared with the poor!"

. . . .

What was the man guilty of?

Why did Christ tell him to share with the poor?

What happened to the man?

. . . .

LUKE 12:16-21

37

FOUR SEEDS

When he went out to sow his seeds
They fell in different spots
The first fell on the wayside
Birds gobbled them with one shot

The second fell on stony ground
They didn't have much root
They looked good, till the heat was on
Then their demise was acute

The third looked better than the rest
They looked like they would make it
But they grew with weeds that took them down
And left them lifeless on the ground

The last seeds fell on good ground
Where they grew strong and true
Their fruit came in abundance
A great harvest was produced

. . . .

What is Jesus telling us with the story of the seeds?

What do the seeds represent?

What happened to the first seeds? The second seeds?
The third seeds? The last seeds?

. . . .

LUKE 8:4-8

38

MEALS WITH THE LOST

He didn't break bread with Pharisees
When He sat down to eat
He was not impressed with them
The self-righteous He did not seek

Instead He ate with outcasts
Whether lunch or dinner
He was no respecter of persons
And preferred the company of sinners

The Pharisees gave Him lots of flak
And they freely criticized
"Why does He eat with sinners?" they asked
But He cut them down to size

"It's not the righteous who need My help.
They think they have it made.
It's the lost ones I've come to save
And help them find the way."

. . . .

Who is this person eating with sinners?

What was He trying to teach the Pharisees?

. . . .

MATTHEW 9:9-12

~ 39 ~

JESUS'
HOMECOMING

Jesus came back to His hometown
Where great miracles He performed
At first His neighbors were impressed
But then they began to scorn

"Isn't this Jesus of Nazareth?
We've known Him from a kid.
He's a carpenter, not a miracle maker.
Who does He think He is?"

They continued to ridicule
And spew their sneering grind
Jesus said, "In this town I will do no miracles.
A prophet has no honor among his own kind."

. . . .

Where was Jesus' hometown?

Why didn't His neighbors believe in Him?

Why did Jesus say that a prophet has no honor among his own kind?

. . . .

MARK 6:1-5

40

MIRACLE OF
THE LOAVES

Many people came out to hear
What Jesus had to say
The day was long and they were hungry
The disciples said, "Send them all away."

In the crowd there was a little boy
Who had some fish and bread
He offered it, but the disciples said,
"Send them away for food instead."

Jesus said, "Tell everyone to sit down."
As He prayed over this meager meal
Heaps of fish and bread grew before their eyes,
And everyone was filled

All the people had more than enough,
Many baskets with leftovers filled
Jesus did this to show God's great power in Him,
So that their faith in Him would build

. . . .

How many fish and loaves of bread did Jesus pray over?

How many people did Jesus feed?

How much was left over?

Why did Jesus perform this miracle?

. . . .

MARK 6:34-44

41

THE SHORT MAN

It's kind of tough to be short
When there are things you want to see
Such was the plight of this short man
So he climbed a Sycamore tree

He wanted to see Jesus
The thronging crowd was in the way
Jesus looked up to where he sat on a limb
And said, "To your house I will go today."

Now this short man was much despised
By the people so intensely
He collected taxes
And they hated him immensely

But Jesus saw something else
In the man He met that day
Who gave away half of all he made
And if he cheated, he would repay

Jesus could see his believing heart
And his words were verification
That he had repented and changed his ways
And the short man found salvation

. . . .

Who is the short man?

Why do you think Jesus wanted to go to his home?

What did the man have to do to receive salvation?

. . . .

LUKE 19:1-10

42

ACTIONS
AND WORDS

The father said, "I need your help
Out in the vineyard today."
The first son said, "No, I won't go.
At home I plan to stay."

But later he put on his working clothes
For he had changed his mind
Into the vineyard he did go
To tend and nurture the vines

The father asked the second son
to go to the vineyard and work
This son said, "Sure I'll go, Dad."
But his duty he did shirk

So which one did his father's will?
The one who said no
but went ahead still

. . . .

What is Jesus teaching in this parable?

What does it mean that our actions speak louder than our words?

. . . .

MATTHEW 21:28-31

43

THE GRAIN

Jesus was walking through a field
Where the wheat stalks hung with grain
His disciples plucked off some to eat
As they talked along the way

The Pharisees got in a huff
Jesus they loved to criticize
"On the Sabbath, you can do no work!"
They spewed their sanctimonious jive

"Don't you know what David did?"
Jesus, looking at them, declared
"When he ate the priest's bread
No condemnation in what he dared."

For God says in His Word
Mercy over sacrifice should abound
The Sabbath was made for man
Not the other way around

· · · · · · · · · · · · · · · · · · ·

Why did the Pharisees condemn Jesus
and His disciples for plucking the grain?

Who is Lord of the Sabbath?

· · · · · · · · · · · · · · · · · · ·

MATTHEW 12:1-8

~ 44 ~

PUBLICAN AND PHARISEE

A proud Pharisee and a publican
To the temple went to pray
The Pharisee told God about all his good works
The publican beat his breast in shame

The Pharisee said,
"I'm glad I'm not like him.
Why I tithe, fast, and pray,
And, I would never ever sin."

The publican bowed and prayed
He would not even lift his eyes,
Crying, "Be merciful to me a sinner!"
It was he, not the Pharisee, who was justified

Jesus said, "If you want to be exalted,
A humble heart must come first.
If you think you're all that great,
Your prayers will not be heard."

· · · · · · · · · · · · · · · · · · ·

Why did Christ say the man was justified?

Why did Jesus say the Pharisee was not justified?

· · · · · · · · · · · · · · · · · · ·

LUKE 18:9-14

45

RENDER TO CAESAR

The Pharisees always tried to trip up Jesus
They would sit and conspire for hours
How they could get Him to misstep
And wipe out His growing power

They knew the people hated tax collectors
And the Romans who exacted their due
They devised a question about taxes
That they were sure Jesus would rue

Thinking Jesus would have to say no
Then they could accuse Him of insurrection
They asked Him, "Should we pay taxes
Into Caesar's tax collections?"

Jesus asked, "Whose picture is on this coin?"
They said, "Why it's Caesar's of course!"
Jesus said, "Then render to Caesar what is Caesar's
And to the Lord what is the Lord's."

The Pharisees were really ticked
Jesus did not stumble
They scattered in a pouty huff
Their little scheme had crumbled

. . . .

What wrong emotion prompted the Pharisees
to want to take away Jesus' power?

Why did Jesus say, "Render to Caesar the things that are Caesar's"?

. . . .

MARK 12:13-17

46

FORGIVENESS

The king came to collect his debts
A debtor who owed him a lot of dough
Cried and begged him to release the debt
The king said, "No! You'll pay what you owe."

Later the king felt sorry for him
Said, "I will cancel your debt. Go free,
You are forgiven the large debt you owe.
I will show you kindness and mercy."

But the debtor, instead of being thankful
And showing others the favor he was shown
When a man couldn't pay a small debt to him
Into prison he was thrown

The king heard of the matter
His anger was inflamed
To the debtor he said, "I forgave your debt
And to this man you couldn't do the same.

Now get away from me, you evil one,
For in prison you will go and stay
Where you will live with what you've done
And be tormented every day."

. . . .

What lesson can we learn from the debtor?

Have we been forgiven a lot?

How do we forgive others?

. . . .

MATTHEW 18:23-35

47

THE LABORERS

They went to work in the early morn
In the vineyard, they worked all day
For a certain wage
That the master agreed to pay

Later in that afternoon
Other workers were employed
For the exact same wage
This left the early workers most annoyed

"We have toiled all day in the sun!"
They cried out in exasperation.
"And you're giving them the same as us!"
They growled in their frustration

The master said, "I don't know why
You are so angry and annoyed.
We agreed upon your wage
And what I pay is my choice.

For everyone gets the same
Whether all day or a part.
It's not about how long you work
But that you make the decision to start."

· · · · · · · · · · · · · · · · ·

What was Jesus teaching the disciples in this parable?

Was it fair to pay the workers the same? Why?

· · · · · · · · · · · · · · · · ·

MATTHEW 20:1-16

∾ 48 ∾

THE TALENTS

Jesus loved to teach with stories
The gifts of talents was one so wise
About how we're each given something
To grow and maximize

Three different guys got talents
5, 2 and 1 they received
To grow for their master
While he was on a leave

"What have you done with what I gave you?"
The master asked when he came back
Two had doubled what they received
One buried his in a sack

The master was livid with this fruitless one
He said, "Man, your time with me is toast!
I am taking away the one talent you have
And giving it to the one with the most!"

. . . .

How many talents did the master give his employees?

Why did one man bury his in the ground?

What is the lesson Jesus is teaching here?

How does fear hold us back?

Why did the one with the most get the talent?

. . . .

MATTHEW 25:14-30

49

THE DEAD ARISE

The sisters lamented and mourned
Their beloved brother three days ago died
His body shrouded and sealed in a tomb
Their tears they could not hide

Jesus had delayed His coming
This added to their woe and distress
If Jesus had come, He would have healed him
And their brother wouldn't have been laid to rest

But once their brother died,
They thought it was too late
Jesus said, "You will see him again."
But they thought death was his fate

Already buried for days,
His body had begun to decompose
They didn't understand that Jesus was God
And by His word, the dead arose

Because of their lack of faith, He wept
Standing at the tomb He called, "Come out now!"
And His once-dead friend walked out fully alive
From then on many believed in His power

· · · · · · · · · · · · · · · · · · ·

Who is the friend whom Jesus raised from the dead?

Why did Jesus not come sooner and heal His friend?

Who asked Jesus to come heal their brother?

Why did Jesus cry?

· · · · · · · · · · · · · · · · · · ·

JOHN 11:1-44

50

WHEN JESUS DIED

When Jesus breathed His final shattered breath
And surrendered His spirit at last
Foretold events came to pass at once
As spoken by the old prophets of past

The temple curtain was ripped asunder
That separated the holiest place
Earthquake shook and thunder roared
And many dead came out of their graves

Roman centurions by the cross
Were dazed and stupefied
They cried, "Surely this was the Son of God
That we have crucified!"

. . . .

What was the symbolism behind the tent being
ripped that separated the Holy of Holies?

What does it mean for us today?

. . . .

MATTHEW 27:50-54

MARK 15:37-39

LUKE 23:45-47

51

TWO TRAVELERS

They were heading toward a village
Sad and discouraged they memorialized
The tragedies of the days before
About Jesus who'd been crucified

Suddenly a stranger joined them
Asking about their conversation
"Don't you know what has transpired?"
They spoke in anguish and desolation

Women came to His tomb
Angels they did see
Who told them He was risen
But we don't know what to believe

The stranger said directly to them
"Why don't you believe?
The prophets said the Christ must suffer
His glorious goal to achieve."

Later He explained the prophecies
That told of His life
When they sat down to eat
He vanished from their sight

The two hurried back to Jerusalem
To tell others they'd seen the Christ
That He truly was risen from the dead
Their joy was greatly multiplied

. . . .

Where were the two men going?

Who was the stranger? Why did He talk with them?

. . . .

LUKE 24:13-35

⤙ 52 ⤚

THE MISSION

With the disciples, Jesus would often speak
About His goal and the mission He must keep
His goal: to do His Father's will
His mission: to lay down His life for the sheep

Jesus told them how He must suffer and die
Peter rebuked him, saying, "Lord, this isn't right!"
Jesus said, "Peter, you know not the things of God.
Get behind me and be quiet."

They didn't comprehend what the Lord was saying
Hoping surely Jesus would restore Israel's glory
And free them from Rome's despotic rule
But God was writing a different story

With a far greater and better conclusion
Than they could ever prepare to endeavor
That God would use Jesus to save not only Israel
But all mankind forever and ever

Jesus accomplished all He said
He died and in three days rose from the grave
Telling the disciples, "Take this message to the world
So that he who hears may believe and be saved."

. . . .

Why did the disciples not want to believe that Jesus would die?

What did they hope Jesus would do?

. . . .

MATTHEW 16:21-24; 28:16-20

ABOUT THE AUTHOR

Sylvia Taylor-Stein

Sylvia is an artist and songwriter who has a special gift for poetry. She wrote her first poem when she was 8, and continued to write through her years in school and college. She wrote all the lyrics and music for her CD of original songs of faith and hope entitled "Pass It Along." It was recorded in 2000 and has since been remastered recently as "Paintings on My Soul."

Sylvia's great love for heroes and heroines in the Bible started when she was about 5 years old, from listening to her grandmother in her Smoky Mountain home. Her Grandma Lottie had a gift for creating excitement and interest in the Bible through her graphic and fascinating storytelling and she created a love in Sylvia for the heroes of the Bible.

Sylvia said, "I never forgot the Bible stories my Grandma taught me, and most of these riddles and rhymes come straight from her stories. My hope is that these riddles and rhymes will help many generations connect and spend time studying God's Word, and will create a generational legacy for grandparents to pass on to their grandchildren."

Sylvia spent over a decade working in the publishing field where she contributed to many publications and articles.

Sylvia currently serves as Executive Director of the Ventura County Ombudsman Program where she advocates for elderly and disabled residents in nursing homes and other long term care facilities. For recognition of her outstanding service in this field, Sylvia has earned the Nonprofit Champion of Healthcare Award for Southern California (2017) and the National Consumer Voice Award for Quality Long-Term Care (2013).

Sylvia and her husband, Marc, live in Southern California and have five children and three grandchildren.

ABOUT THE ILLUSTRATOR

Wilson Gandolpho

Wilson Gandolpho lives in São Paulo, Brazil, where he works for large media outlets producing daily comic strips with his characters. He recently embarked on an international journey with the goal of expanding his work and reaching challenges beyond local boundaries. It was this goal that made him apply to do the illustrations for *Bible Times in Riddles & Rhymes*.

Wilson says, "When I saw the ad, I never believed I would get the job, but the requirement to know the Bible caught my attention and I think God made me apply. It was clear that this work was not something common. I had never done a job at this level of art and with this amount of scenes. Studying the Bible to draw the scenes also made me evolve in the Scriptures. I have realized that the Lord has been by my side, testing me, teaching me, and preparing me for the future He has for me. I am deeply grateful for the opportunity I was given to illustrate *Bible Times in Riddles & Rhymes*."